Mikhail Chudnov

Kalimba Lessons for Beginners with 50 Songs

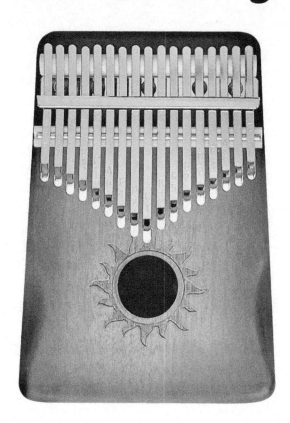

Theory and Practice + Online Videos

Messages about typos, errors, inaccuracies and suggestions for improving the quality are gratefully received at:
avgustaudartseva@gmail.com

CONTENTS

About Kalimba

Welcome to the world of the kalimba, a musical instrument that will capture your imagination and help you discover the magic of music! Here is a quick overview of interesting facts about the kalimba for those who are just beginning their musical journey:

Origin and heritage: the kalimba has a long history that originates in Africa. The instrument is part of many cultures and has recently gained popularity around the world.

Metal plates: the main part of the kalimba is made up of metal plates or lames that create the sound. They vary in size and shape, and their combination produces magical music.

Easy to play: the kalimba is an ideal instrument for beginners. It requires no special training and allows you to start playing quickly.

Portability: many kalimbas are easy to take with you. Their compact size allows you to play music anywhere.

Emotional effect: the kalimba can evoke different feelings in you, from joy to relaxation. The sounds of this instrument help you express your feelings.

Music and therapy: the kalimba sounds are used in music therapy to alleviate stress and release tension.

Widespread use: the kalimba can be heard in various genres of music, from African to pop music.

Sound perception: playing the kalimba helps improve your perception of musical sounds. You will learn to distinguish between different notes and their nuances.

Experimenting with rhythm: the kalimba is a great tool for learning rhythms. You can create your own rhythmic melodies and improve your skills in playing in different tempos.

Expressing creativity: With the kalimba you can express your own musical ideas and feelings. This instrument will be your faithful friend in your creative endeavors.

Communicating through music: playing the kalimba makes it easier for you to understand and interact with music. It will become your "other" language.

Exploring cultures: The kalimba connects many cultures around the world. By studying it, you will learn more about different traditions and musical heritage.

Let the kalimba be your faithful friend on your musical journey. You will get the opportunity to explore many different aspects of music and take in all of its magic. Always remember that music is your personal story that you create with one touch of the keys (lames) of the kalimba. Enjoy music and discover new possibilities!

Musical Note

Before starting to play the kalimba, let's review the basics of music theory:

A musical note is a symbol that represents a particular sound. On the kalimba, notes are labeled with certain letters: **C, D, E, F, G, A, B.**

A musical note is written on a musical staff. The staff is a horizontal grid where musical notes and other musical symbols are placed representing a melody or composition. The musical notes are arranged on staff lines and in the spaces between them.

Typically, a staff consists of five lines and four spaces. This is commonly known as a five-line staff. The notes are arranged on these lines and spaces according to their pitch. Higher placed notes sound higher and notes that are placed lower sound lower.

A musical staff is used to record musical notes, rhythm, harmony, and other musical elements in a clear and standardized form so that musicians can read and perform music.

The Treble Clef

The Stave (Staff)

The treble clef, also known as the G-clef is one of the symbols used in music notation to determine the pitch of the notes on the sheet music.

The treble clef is suitable for recording the notes of the first, second, and third octaves.

The standard kalimba has only the first and second octaves.

Notes of the first octave

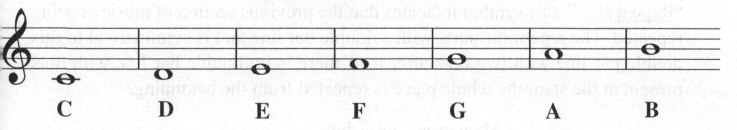

C   D   E   F   G   A   B

Notes of the second octave

C   D   E   F   G   A   B

Notes of the third octave

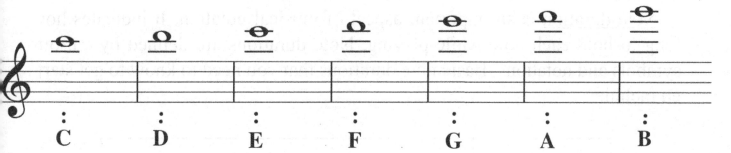

C   D   E   F   G   A   B

Music Measure

A measure in music is one "slice" of musical text that goes from a downbeat to the next downbeat. A measure (or a bar) can be simple (with one downbeat) or compound (with several strong and relatively strong beats). This depends on the time signature of a given song.

In music notation, a measure (or a bar) is the interval between two vertical lines on a sheet of music. It defines the structure of a piece of music and helps musicians keep the beat. These vertical lines, which mark the measure, can vary in appearance:

Bar line: these are used to divide a piece of music into different segments and help musicians find their way around music.

A final double bar line is placed at the end of a piece of music and marks the end of the piece.

The bold double bar line with two dots in front of it is also called the "Repeat sign": this symbol indicates that the previous section of music is being repeated. The repetition starts with a double bar line that is symmetrical to this double bar line with two dots after it. If there is no double bar line with dots present at the start, the whole piece is repeated from the beginning.

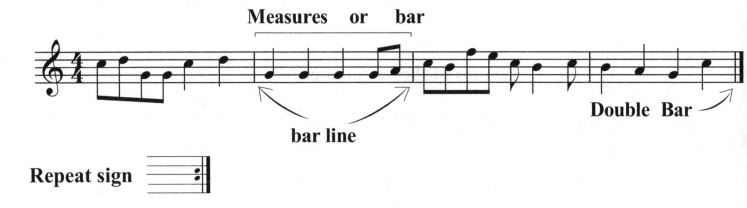

Note Duration

Note duration is an important aspect of musical notation. It indicates how long to hold each note while playing. Note durations are defined by various symbols and notations. Basic note durations that you need to know to get started include:

Whole note	o = 4 beats (1 and 2 and 3 and 4 and)
Half note	𝅗𝅥 = 2 beats (1 and 2 and)
Quarter note	♩ = 1 beat 1 and
Eighth note	♪ = 1/2 beat ♪ ♪ = 1 beat 1 and
Sixteenth note	♬ = 1/4 beat ♬♬ = 1 beat 1 and

Musical Rest

In music, <u>rest</u> is a rhythmic pause or a period of silence when the performer does not play a single note or rhythm pattern. Rests are as important as notes, and they are used to create rhythmic placement and reinforce musical structure.

Music rests have their own symbols in musical notation, and each rest symbol indicates how long that particular rest is. The main types of rests include:

Rests		Notes
Whole rest	▬ = 𝅝	Whole note
Half rest	▬ = 𝅗𝅥	Half note
Quarter rest	𝄽 = ♩	Quarter note
Eighth rest	𝄾 = ♪	Eighth note
Sixteenth rest	𝄿 = 𝅘𝅥𝅯	Sixteenth note

Time Signature

<u>Time signature</u> in music is a sign that shows how long a measure lasts in a given piece of music and also how many notes or rests "fit" in that measure. Time signature determines the rhythmic structure of a piece of music and tells the performer how to arrange notes and rests in that piece.

Time signature is represented as a fraction, where the top number indicates the number of notes (or rests) in a measure, and the bottom number indicates which note value is counted as a beat.

Most common time signatures:

The "two-four" time signature $\frac{2}{4}$

The "two-four" time signature in musical notation indicates that only two notes (beats) can be placed in one measure, each having the value of a quarter note. This time signature can also be represented with a one-half note, four eighth notes, or eight sixteenth notes. In the context of the rhythm and meter of a piece of music, this time signature defines the beat count as "1-and-2-and" of individual rhythmic units in one measure, and does not allow more or less than this value.

The "three-four" time signature $\frac{3}{4}$

The "three-four" size in musical notation indicates that only three notes can be placed in one measure, each having the note value of a quarter. This signature can also represent one half note with a dot (if you see a dot placed right next to a note, it means that the duration of that note is increased by one-half of the given duration ♩. (in this figure, the beat count of that note would be as follows: "1-and-2-and-3-and")), six eighth notes, or twelve sixteenth notes. In the context of the rhythm and meter of a piece of music, this time signature defines the beat count as "1-and-2-and-3-and" of individual rhythmic units in one measure, and does not allow more or less than this value.

The "four-four" time signature $\frac{4}{4} = \mathbf{C}$

The "four-four" signature in musical notation indicates that one measure can only accommodate four notes, each of which has the value of a quarter note. This signature can also be represented by two one-half notes, four eighth notes, or sixteen sixteenth notes. In the context of the rhythm and meter of a piece of music, this time signature defines the beat count as "1-and-2-and-3-and-4-and" of individual rhythmic units in one measure, and does not allow more or less than this value.

Examples:

Practice Exercises

Music exercises are specifically designed assignments and practice exercises designed to develop necessary skills and teach music. They can include various aspects of music education such as instrument technique, rhythm, harmony, melody, arranging and improvisation. Musical exercises can focus on developing specific skills or on the general development of musical awareness. Playing musical exercises on an instrument accomplishes the following goals:

Developing technical skills: musical exercises help improve instrument technique, including hand coordination, finger dexterity, and accuracy.

Teaching musical literacy: by playing through the exercises, the musician can learn and improve the skills of reading musical notation, which is an important aspect of music education.

Aural development: playing exercises helps to improve aural skills such as recognizing melodies, chords and rhythms.

Enhancing musical creativity: playing an instrument allows musicians to develop their musical imagination and experiment with sounds and melodies.

Preparing for performance: exercises help improve musical confidence and readiness to perform in front of an audience.

In general, musical exercises contribute to the development of a musician and help her become more skilled and expressive in musical performance.

Here are a few exercises that you should do daily to improve your technique and ability to play an instrument:

1.

2.

3.

If one note is placed above the other in musical notation, it means that both notes must be played at the same time on the instrument you are playing:

4.

5.

Slur and Slurred Notes

Slurs and slurred notes are important concepts in music, especially in musical notation. Let's dissect these concepts:

A slur is a musical sign that indicates the need to play two or more notes smoothly, without a break in between. Slurs connect notes with the same value and allow them to be played as one string of notes. This helps create musical phrases and *legato* effect.

If you see two identical notes under a slur, it means that the first note is plucked and the second note is counted without being plucked again.

The slur can also be applied to more notes, creating more complex musical phrases.

Tone, Half Tone (or step, half step)

In music, the terms "tone" and "half tone" refer to the musical interval that defines the distance between two musical notes.

A tone (or whole tone) is a standard musical interval that corresponds to the distance of one full note on a musical ruler or the key of an instrument. In other words, if you move from one note to another by one tone, you move one full key on a piano or up or down one line in musical notation.

A half tone is then a half of a standard musical interval. It corresponds to a distance of one key on the piano or one intermediate line in musical notation. Thus, a half tone is smaller than a tone and is the smallest musical interval in our musical system.

Tones and half tones are used to determine the pitch of sounds and to construct musical scales and chords. They play an important role in musical theory and practice, helping musicians create harmonious and melodic music.

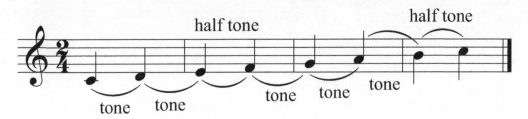

all half tones

all half tones

Sharp, Flat, Natural (notation and key signature)

A sharp and a flat are two alteration signs in music that are used to change the pitch of a note. Here is what they mean:

Sharp (♯) - raises the pitch of a note by one semitone. For example, if you have the note C and add a sharp to it, you get the note C# (C-sharp).

Flat (♭) - lowers the pitch of a note by one semitone. For example, if you have a D note and add a flat to it, you get a D-flat.

Natural (♮)- cancels out the effects of either sharp or flat.

These signs of alteration are used to create different key signatures and chords in music; to change the pitch of a note and thus to achieve different musical expressions. They are also used to avoid awkward note sequences.

Sharp, flat and natural signs are written before the note.

I sincerely appreciate your focus on studying music theory to better understand it. I trust that you have grasped everything that has been laid out in this book. In that case, we can definitely continue on to the practical application section.

ALL VIDEOS (Playlist)

All videos are also in the same playlist on YouTube:

or link:

cutt.ly/xwTgoy7I

Messages about typos, errors, inaccuracies and suggestions for improving the quality are gratefully received at:
avgustaudartseva@gmail.com

1. Alphabet Song

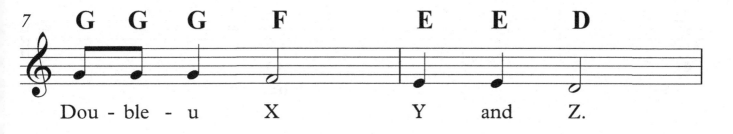

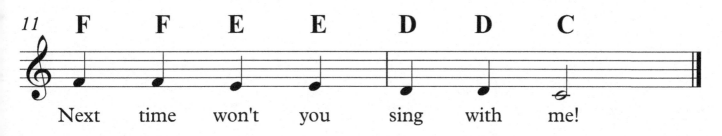

2. God Is So Good

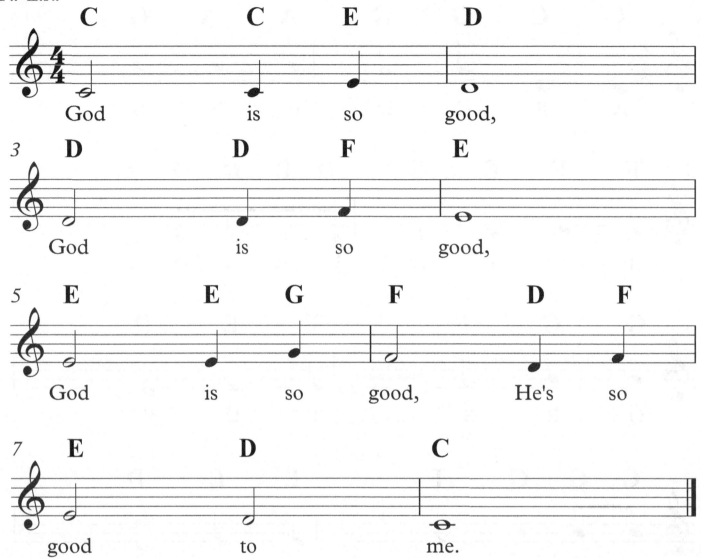

3. O When The Saints

4. Sleep, Baby Sleep

2. Sleep, baby, sleep.
   Our cottage vale is deep.
   The little lamb is on the green
   With snowy fleece so soft and clean
   Sleep, baby, sleep.

5. A-Tisket, A-Tasket

6. Skip To My Lou

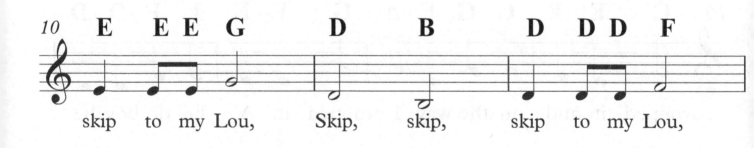

7. Mary Had A Little Lamb

8. *This Old Man*

9. Rain, Rain, Go Away

10. Little Sally Water

Lit - tle Sal - ly Wa - ter sit - ting in a

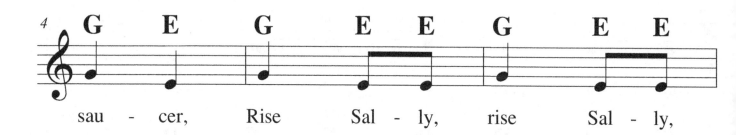

sau - cer, Rise Sal - ly, rise Sal - ly,

wipe a - way your tears, Sal - ly, Turn to the

east, Sal - ly, Turn to the west, Sal - ly Turn to the

one, that you love the best Sal - ly.

11. Silver Moon Boat

12. Hickory Dickory Dock

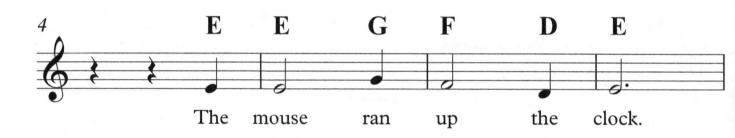

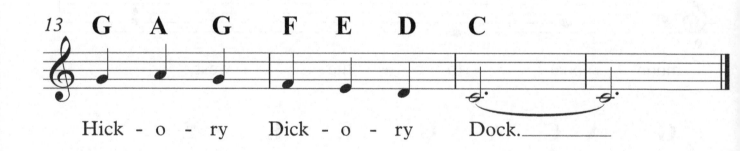

13. Ring Around The Rosie

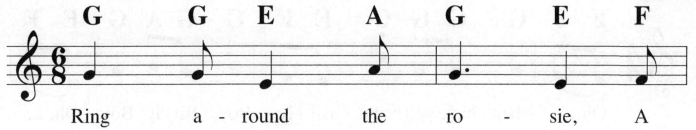

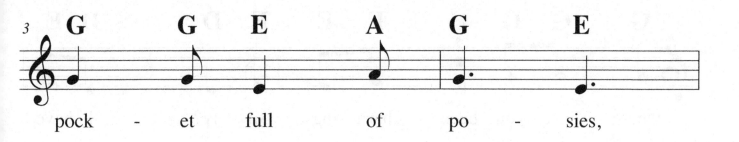

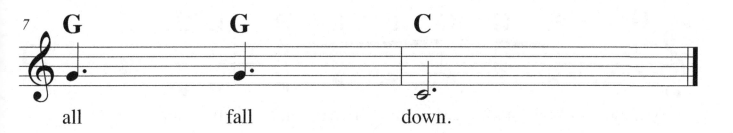

14. Billy Boy

Oh, where have you been, Bil - ly Boy, Bil - ly Boy, Oh,

where have you been charm - ing Bil - ly? I have

been to seek a wife, She's the joy of my life, She's a

young thing and can - not leave her mo - ther

15. London Bridge Is Falling Down

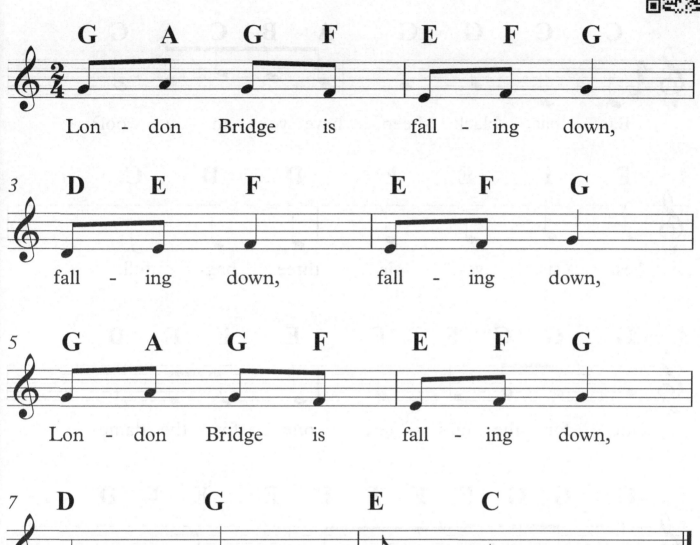

16. Baa, Baa, Black Sheep

Baa, baa, black sheep, have you an - y wool?

Yes, sir, yes, sir, three bags full.

One for the mas - ter, one for the dame.

One for the lit - tle boy who lives down the lane.

Baa, baa, black, sheep have you an - y wool?

Yes, sir, yes, sir, three bags full.

17. Joy To The World

Joy to the world! The Lord is come; Let

earth re - ceive her King; Let

ev - 'ry__ he - art pre - pa - re Him ro - om. And

heaven and na - tu - re sing. And heaven and na - tu - re sing. And

heaven and hea - ven and na - ture sing.

18. Silent Night

19. The First Noel

The first No - el the An-gel did say Was to

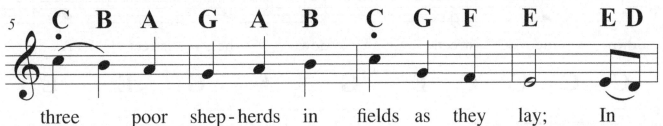

three poor shep-herds in fields as they lay; In

fields where they lay keep-ing their sheep, On a

cold win-ter's night that was so deep. No -

el No - el No - el No - el,

Born is the King of Is - ra - el!

20. Buffalo Gals

21. Humpty Dumpty

Hump - ty Dump - ty sat on a wall.

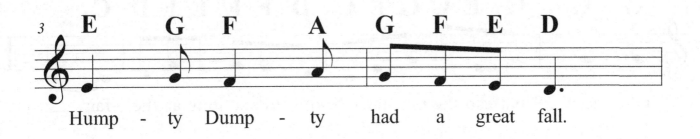

Hump - ty Dump - ty had a great fall.

All the king's hor - ses and all the king's men

could - n't put Hump - ty to - ge - ther a - gain.

22. Oh, Dear! What Can The Matter Be?

Oh, dear! What can the mat-ter be? Oh, dear! What can the mat-ter be?

Oh, dear! What can the mat-ter be? John-ny's so long at the fair.___

He pro-mised to buy me a trin-ket to please me, And

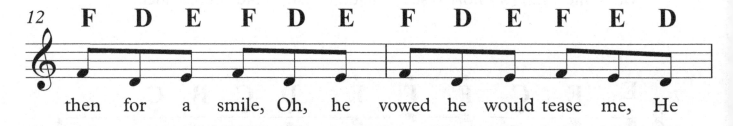

then for a smile, Oh, he vowed he would tease me, He

pro-mised to bring me a bunch of red ro-ses to

tie up my bon-nie brown hair._____

23. She'll Be Coming 'Round The Mountain

G A C C C C A G E G

She'll be co - ming 'round the moun - tain when she

C C D E E E E G G F E

comes, She'll be co - ming 'round the moun - tain when she

D G F E E E E D C C C

comes, She'll be co - ming 'round the moun - tain, She'll be

A A A A D C B A

co - ming 'round the moun - tain, She'll be

G G C D E D A B C

co - ming 'round the moun - tain when she comes.

24. Aura Lee

Music: George R. Poulton
Lyrics: W. W. Fosdick

25. Oh! Susanna

Steven Foster

I____ came from A - la - ba - ma, with my

ba - ma, with my knee. I'm____ goin' to Loui - si -

a - na, My ____ true love for to

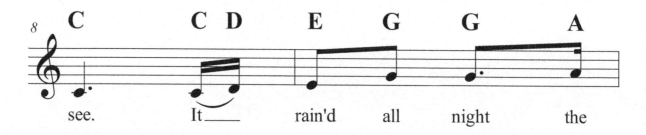

see. It____ rain'd all night the

day I left, The wea - ther it was

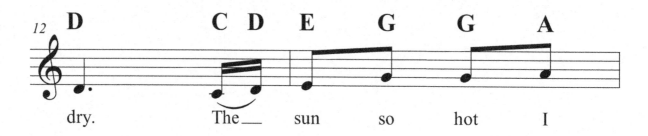

dry. The___ sun so hot I

froze to death, Su - san - na don't you

cry. Oh! Su - san - na, Oh

don't you cry for me. I've come from A - la -

ba - ma, with my ban - jo on my knee.

26. Solidarity Forever

The Battle Hymn of Republic

Traditional

G G G G G F E G Ċ Ḋ

When the u - nion's in - spi - ra - tion through the

Ė Ė Ė Ḋ Ċ Ċ B A A B

wor - kers' blood shall run, there can be no po - wer

Ċ B Ċ A G A G E

grea - ter an - y - where be - neath the

G G G G G G F

sun; Yet what force on earth is

E G Ċ Ḋ Ė Ė Ė Ḋ

weak - er - than the fee - ble strength of

Ċ Ċ Ċ Ḋ Ḋ

one, for the u - nion

27. Can Can

Jacques Offenbach

28. Up on the Housetop

Benjamin Hanby

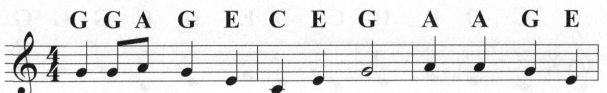

Up on the house-top rein-deer pause, Out jumps good old

San - ta Claus; Down through the chim-ney with lots of toys,

All for the lit-tle ones, Christ-mas joys. Ho, ho, ho,

Who would-n't go? Ho, ho, ho, Who would-n't go,___

Up on the house - top click, click, click,

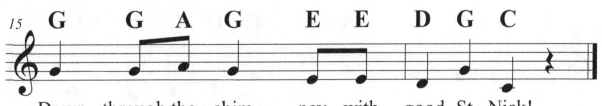

Down through the chim - ney with good St. Nick!

29. The Wassail Song

Music: Traditional
Words: New Oxford Book of Carols

C D E D C D E D C G G G

Here we come a - was - sai-ling a - mong the leaves so

G A A G E G F E

green. Here we come a - wand' - ring, so

D C D E F E F G Ċ A

fa - ir to be seen. Love and joy come to

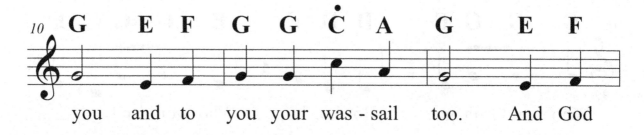

G E F G G Ċ A G E F

you and to you your was - sail too. And God

G A E F D C B C D E C

bless you and send you a Hap - py New

F E F G A E F D C B C

Year, and God sent you a Hap - py New Year!

30. Jack And Jill

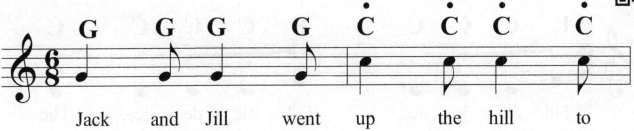

G G G G Ċ Ċ Ċ Ċ

Jack and Jill went up the hill to

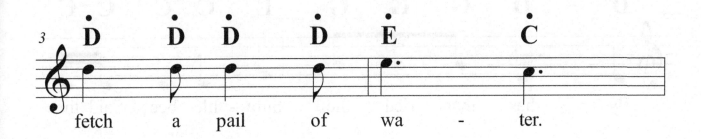

Ḋ Ḋ Ḋ Ḋ Ė Ċ

fetch a pail of wa - ter.

G G G G A A A A

Jack fell down and broke his crown and

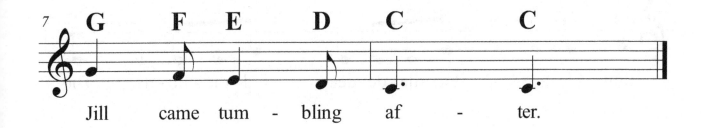

G F E D C C

Jill came tum - bling af - ter.

31. Fiddle-De-De

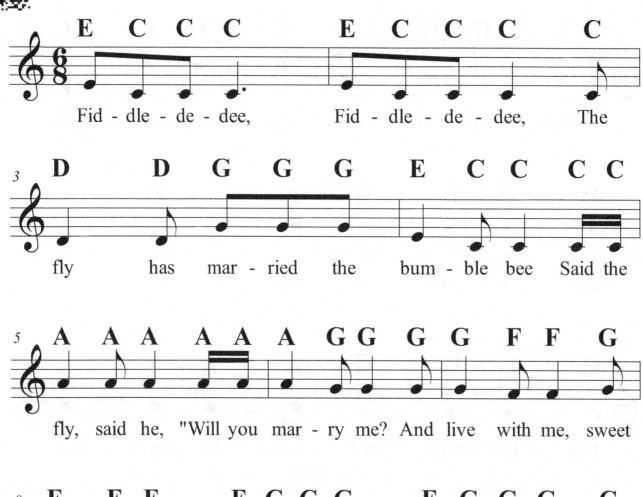

| E | C | C | C | | E | C | C | C | | C |
Fid - dle - de - dee, Fid - dle - de - dee, The

| D | D | G | G | G | E | C | C | C | C |
fly has mar - ried the bum - ble bee Said the

| A | A | A | A | A | A | G | G | G | G | F | F | G |
fly, said he, "Will you mar - ry me? And live with me, sweet

| F | E | E | E | C | C | E | C | C | C | C |
bum - ble bee?" Fid - dle - de - dee Fid - dle - de - dee, The

| D | D | G | G | G | E | C | C |
fly has mar - ried the bum - ble bee.

2. Said the Bee, says she
   "I'll live under your wing
   You'll never know I carry a sting"
   Fiddle-de-dee, Fiddle-de-dee
   The Fly has married the Bumble Bee

32. Marine's Hymn

From the halls of Mon - te - zu - ma, To the shores of

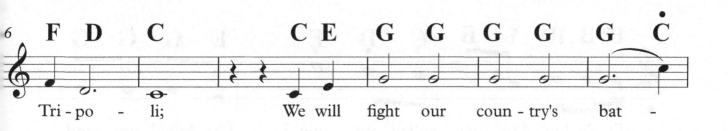

Tri - po - li; We will fight our coun - try's bat -

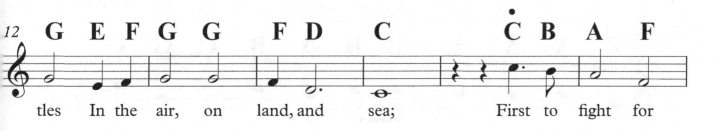

tles In the air, on land, and sea; First to fight for

right and free - dom And to keep our ho - nor clean:___

___ We are proud to claim the ti -

-tle of U - ni - ted States Ma - rines.___

33. Little Brown Jug

My wife and I lived all a - lone In a

lit - tle log hut we called our own; She loved gin, and

I loved rum; I tell you what, we'd lots of fun.

Ha, ha, ha, you and me, "Lit-tle brown jug,"don't

I love thee; Ha, ha, ha, you and me

"Lit - tle brown jug," don't I love thee.

34. Twinkle, Twinkle, Little Star

Twin - kle, twin-kle, lit - tle star,   How I won-der what you are.   Up a - bove the world so high,

Like a dia-mond   in the sky,   Twin-kle,twin-kle, lit - tle star,   How I won-der   what you are.

35. Red River Valley

From this val - ley they say - you are go - ing.   I - will miss your brigh

eyes and sweet smile   For - they say - you are tak - ing the sun - shine.

That has bright - ened our path - for a while.

36. Ode to Joy

E E F G G F E D C C D E E D D   E E F G G F E D

C C D E D C C   D E C D E F E C   D E F E D

C E C   E E F G G F E D C C D E D C C

37. Holiday

M. Chudnovskiy

CGFEDE GFED DAGFEF GABC F A F G B G

CBAGAG FCFA CGFEDE GFED DAGFEF

GABC G CG FAF ECBAGF ECEC

38. Puzzles

M. Chudnovskiy

CG A E D E   G F F D   D A   F F E F G A B A   A   F   A   F   G   E   G   C B

A E A G F C F A   A   C G F E F E   G D E D   D A   G F G F G A B A

A G F G   F A E F E A   B A G F E C D C   C

39. Wind

M. Chudnovskiy

CCBA BAGF CCBA BAGF DCBA BAGF ECBA GFED

CCBA BAGF CEGC BAG F EC BA GFED EDCD C

40. Blue eyes

M. Chudnovskiy

A B F   G F E D E F C A C   B A G A   E A G F   F B A G

F C B A G E   F D F E   A B   F   G F E D E F C A C

B G F E C D   E A G F   F B A G   F C B A G E   F D E C

41. Passion

M. Chudnovskiy

A A B A   A G E   A A B A   A G E   A A B A   A A B A   A G A   B
                                                                G

G G A G   G A B   G G A G   G A B   G G A G   G G A G   G A B A G

E D C C   A   A   A G A G   G   G   G A B   A

A A B A   A G E   A A B A   A G E   A A B A   A A B A   A G B   C
                                                                G

42. For your heart

M. Chudnovskiy

CBAGF A GAGFEDC CBAGF A GAGABCD
C   C   F   E   F

EDCBAGFED DCBAGFEDC CBAGFEDCD EFGABCD
G   F   E   C

EDCBAGFED DCBAGFEDC CBAGFEDCD EDCGC
G   F   E   E

43. Beauty

M. Chudnovskiy

E F G C G E F G C G B A G A G F E D E D E F B F
  E   E   F

D E F B F E F G F A G F A B B B E F G C G E F G C
    F   D   E   E

B A G A G F E F G A E C B A B B A G A F G E G D E
                    E

F A G B A G G F A E C B A B B A G A F G E G D E E B A A G F F

E F G C G E F G C G B A G A G F E D E
    E   E

D E F B F D E F B F E F G F A G F A C C C
    F   F

44. Autumn

M. Chudnovskiy

45. Lullaby

M. Chudnovskiy

46. Heavenly Rain

M. Chudnovskiy

FAGFE GAGFE F FAGFE GAGFG A BGABAGF

A F G A G F E F C E D E F G B G A B A G F

A F G A G F E F G F E F G C

47. An Angel Descends

M. Chudnovskiy

F A F B F A F C A G F E A G G A F A F E G E A E G E B

F E D C F E E F G F E G F F G A C F G A C

B G G F B G G F G A G F F

48. Home sweet home

M. Chudnovskiy

CE FE AGFE   DEFEAGFE   F G A B   C   CE FE AG FE

DEFEAGFE   F F G G   C   FGAFA GFE   FGAFA GFE   G B   C

49. Flowers of the soul

M. Chudnovskiy

50. For mom

M. Chudnovskiy

51. Coquette

M. Chudnovskiy

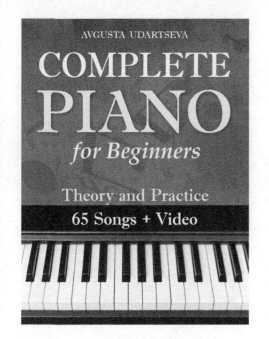

ISBN: 979-8361128570

ASIN: B0BKYHL7PC

Learning to play your favorite songs on the piano is easy!

Today the piano is pobably the most popular musical instrument in the world. Playing this instrument will give you an unforgettable experience.

The book contains musical theory, practical exercises, and 65 popular songs for adults.

The author of the book, Avgusta Udartseva, is a close friend of mine, and so I can wholeheartedly recommend to you her book for learning the piano!

United States **United Kingdom** **Canada**

ISBN: 979-8386419004

ASIN: B0BXMX7ZVN

- Learning step by step: starting with more simple tunes, then gradually moving to more complex songs;
- Includes music theory, instrument history, practice, recommendations and many entertaining songs;
- Learn the position of the body and hands, how to breathe properly and play easily;
- Letters above each note and simple explanations;
- Convenient large US Letter print size;
- Video accompaniment to all lessons by direct link inside the book;
- 2-in-1 Book: Recorder lessons and video + 60 Songs.

United States **United Kingdom** **Canada**

And it's great for adults

Made in the USA
Las Vegas, NV
10 November 2024